Happy birthday!

Bon anniversaire!

Mary Risk
Pictures by Lucy Keijser
French story by Jacqueline Jansen

b small publishing

It's my birthday.

C'est mon anniversaire.

Here are all my friends.
Hi! Hello! Come in, everyone!

Voilà tous mes amis.
Salut! Bonjour! Entrez tous!

All these presents for me?
What a brilliant mask!

Tous ces cadeaux pour moi?
Quel masque génial!

And I love this dinosaur!

Et j'adore ce dinosaure!

Let's blow some bubbles.
Aren't they lovely?

Si on faisait des bulles de savon?
Elles sont belles, non?

Whoosh!

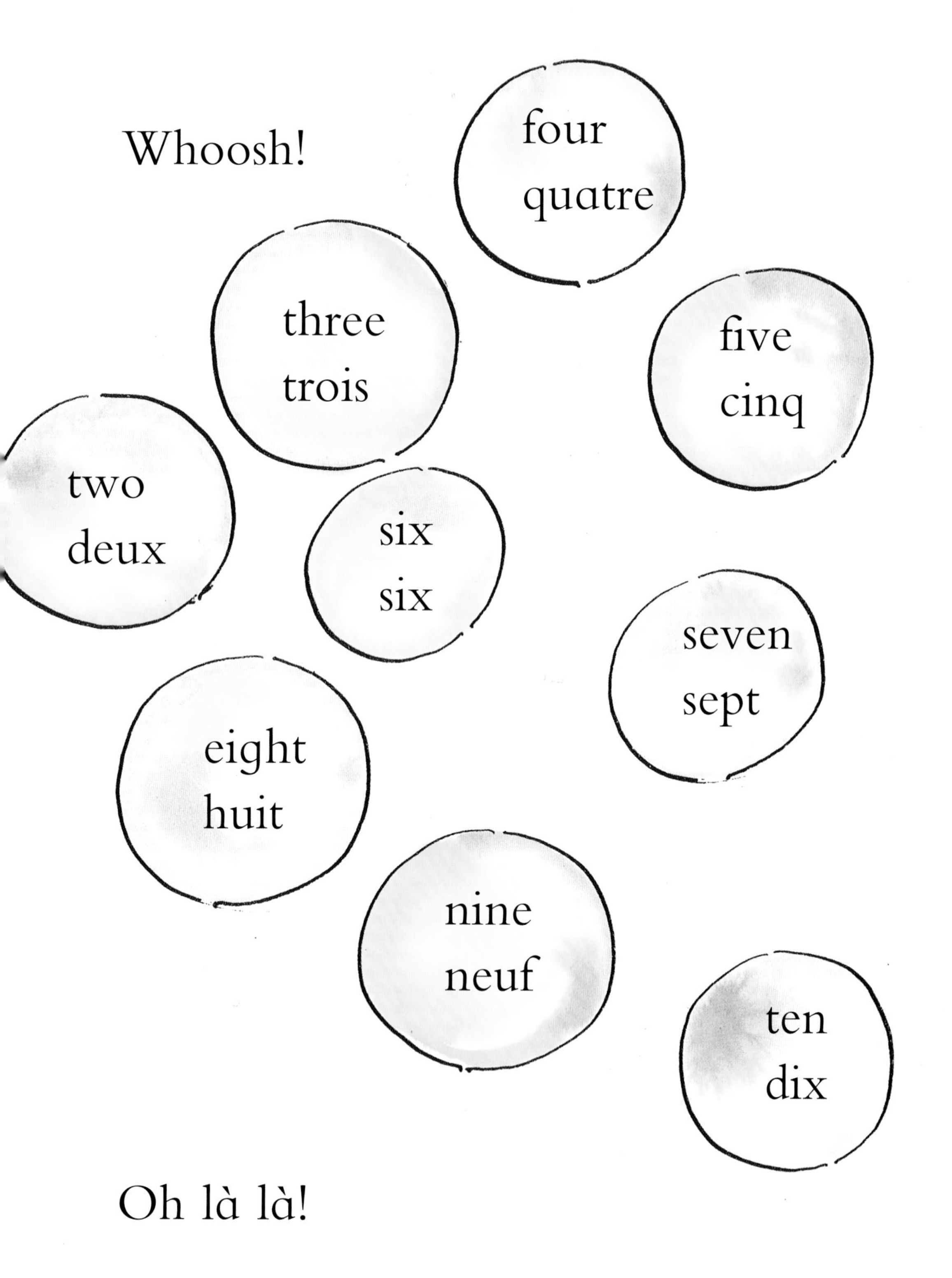

Oh là là!

Where have they all gone?

Où sont-elles passées?

Oh! look at Sarah!

Eh! Regardez Sarah!

Balloons!
Can I have one?

Des ballons!
Est ce que je peux en avoir un?

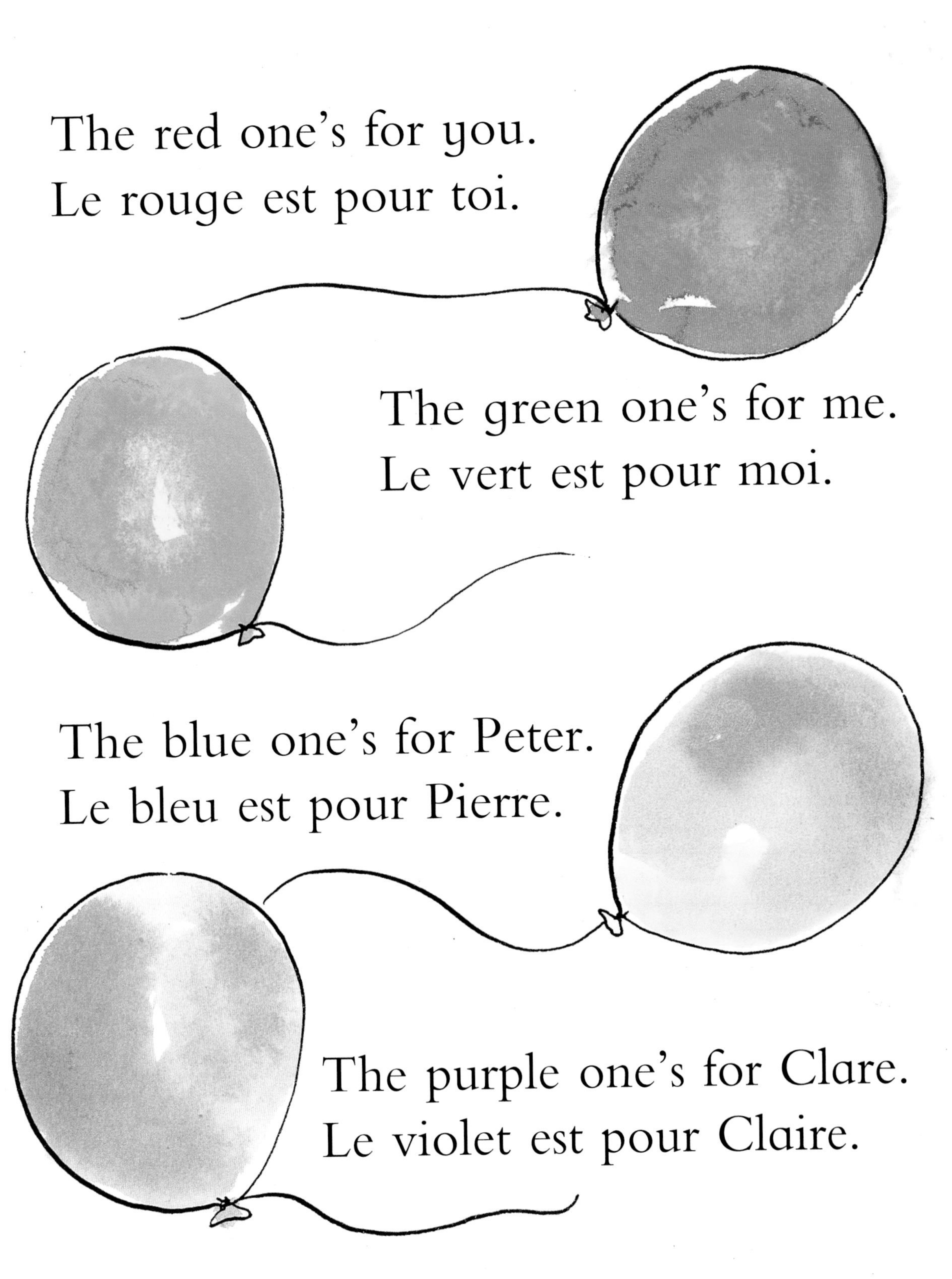

The red one's for you.
Le rouge est pour toi.

The green one's for me.
Le vert est pour moi.

The blue one's for Peter.
Le bleu est pour Pierre.

The purple one's for Clare.
Le violet est pour Claire.

This is fantastic!
This is fun!

Ça c'est super!
Ça c'est marrant!

Oh dear! Goodbye, balloons!

Oh mon dieu! Au revoir, les ballons!

Have you lost your balloon?
Never mind, don't cry!

Tu as perdu ton ballon?
Ce n'est pas grave! Ne pleure pas!

Are you hungry?
Have some cake.

Vous avez faim? Prenez du gâteau.

Are you thirsty?
Have a drink.

Tu as soif? Sers-toi à boire.

That was a lovely party.
Thank you for having us.

C'était une chouette fête.
Merci pour l'invitation.

Look! The balloons!

Regardez! Les ballons!

Goodbye!

Au revoir!

Pronouncing French

Don't worry if your pronunciation isn't quite correct. The important thing is to be willing to try. The pronunciation guide here will help but it cannot be completely accurate:

- Read the guide as naturally as possible, as if it were British English.
- Put stress on the letters in *italics* e.g. lombool-*onss*.
- Don't roll the r at the end of the word, for example in the French word **le** (the): ler.

If you can, ask a French person to help and move on as soon as possible to speaking the words without the guide.

Words Les Mots

leh moh

happy birthday!

bon anniversaire!

boh an-ee-vair-*sair*

cake

le gâteau

ler gat-*o*

present

le cadeau

ler cad-*o*

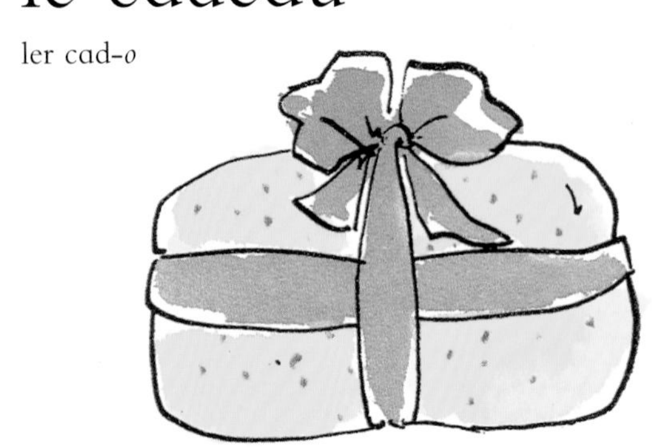

balloon
le ballon
ler bah-*loh*

mask
le masque
ler mask

dinosaur
le dinosaure
ler deeno-*zor*

bubble
la bulle de savon
lah b'yool der sav*oh*

hi
salut
sal-*yoo*

hello
bonjour
boh-*shoor*

thank you
merci
mair*see*

goodbye
au revoir
oh r'v*wah*

friend
l'ami, l'amie
lam*ee*, lam*ee*

lovely
chouette
shoo-*et*

brilliant
génial
shen-*yal*

fantastic
super
s'yoo*pair*

fun
marrant
marr*oh*

party
la fête
lah fett

red
rouge
roo-jsh

purple
violet
vee-o-*leh*

blue
bleu
bl'

green
vert
vair

A simple guide to pronouncing this French story

C'est mon anniversaire.
seh mon an-ee-vair-*sair*
Voilà tous mes amis.
vwul-*a* too meh zam*ee*
Salut! Bonjour! Entrez tous!
sal*yoo*, boh-*shoor*, *on*treh tooss
Tous ces cadeaux pour moi?
too seh cad-*o* poor mwah
Quel masque génial!
kel mask shen-*yal*
Et j'adore ce dinosaure!
eh shah-*door* ser deeno-*zor*
Si on faisait des bulles de savon?
see oh feh-*seh* deh b'yool der sav*oh*
Elles sont belles, non?
el soh bel, noh
un, deux, trois, quatre, cinq, six, sept, huit, neuf, dix
ahn, der, trwah, catr', sank, seess, set, weet, nerf, deess
Oh là là!
o, lah, lah
Où sont-elles passées?
oo son tel pass-*eh*
Eh! Regardez Sarah!
eh, rer-gard-*eh* sah-*rah*
Des ballons!
deh bah-*loh*
Est-ce que je peux en avoir un?
essker sh' per on avwah ahn
Le rouge est pour toi.
ler roo-jsh eh poor twah
Le vert est pour moi.
ler vair eh poor mwah
Le bleu est pour Pierre.
ler bl' eh poor pee-*air*
Le violet est pour Claire.
ler vee-o-*leh* eh poor claire
Ça c'est super!
sah seh s'yoo*pair*
Ça c'est marrant!
seh marr*oh*
Oh mon dieu!
oh moh d'yer
Au revoir, les ballons!
oh r'v*wah* leh bah-*loh*
Tu as perdu ton ballon?
too ah pair*doo* toh bah-*loh*
Ce n'est pas grave! Ne pleure pas!
ser neh pah grahv, ner pler pah
Vous avez faim?
vooz av*eh* fah
Prenez du gâteau.
pr'n*eh* dew gat-*o*
Tu as soif?
too ah swuf
Sers-toi à boire.
sair twah ah bwah
C'était une chouette fête.
seh-*tet* yoon shoo-*et* fet
Merci pour l'invitation
*mair*see poor lanveet-assee-*oh*
Regardez! Les ballons!
rer-gard-*eh*, leh bah-*loh*
Au revoir!
oh r'v*wah*